BOG
BOILS & BELLY
BUTTONS

BOGEYS, BOILS & BELLY BUTTONS

JIM & DUNCAN ELDRIDGE

Illustrated by Graham Round

RED FOX

A Red Fox Book

Published by Random House Children's Books
20 Vauxhall Bridge Road, London SW1V 2SA

A division of Random House UK Ltd
London   Melbourne   Sydney   Auckland
Johannesburg and agencies throughout the world

1 3 5 7 9 10 8 6 4 2

First published in Great Britain by Beaver Books 1986

Red Fox edition 1999

Printed and bound in Norway by AiT Trondheim AS

RANDOM HOUSE UK Limited Reg. No. 954009

ISBN 0 09 944750 9

CONTENTS

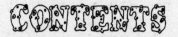

HORRIBLE HUMANS

Acne, worst case of   The worst case of acne on record is that of Henri le Toulouse, aged 15, of Lyons, France, in 1957. His face was so pitted and cratered that he was able to grate large amounts of cheese on both sides of his face at the same time and hired it out as a cheese-grater to a restaurant in his home town. His unusual employment came to an end only when some of the restaurant's customers complained of crusty bits on the cheese sauce, and the Public Health Officer was called in.

Armpits, smelliest The smelliest armpits belonged to an air hostess working out of Heathrow Airport. Every time she raised her arms to indicate the overhead lights, the smell knocked unconscious the passengers nearest to her. She was discovered as the cause only after seventeen planes she served on had been taken out of service, full of unconscious passengers, and checked for fuel leaks.

Beard, largest The largest beard ever known belonged to Fred Smith, who lived in Birmingham. It reached beyond his feet and trailed along yards behind him. It was because of his beard that he got a part-time job as a road sweeper. He was later sacked from this because passing drivers complained of crashing into 'that large hedge tied around his chin'. Apparently Mr Smith's massive beard had accumulated a large quantity of wildlife over the years, including a rare breed of bird that had established a nest just beneath his chin. He died after one of the birds, mistaking him for a predator, pecked his eyes and chin off. His beard was later donated to a wildlife museum.

Did you know that a gorilla can fart five times louder than a human being?

Belch, strongest Earthquake experts in San Francisco, California, recorded a reading of seven on the Richter Scale in 1961, causing many families to flee the city. They later found out that the violent tremor that had shaken the city was not an earthquake but the Deputy Mayor belching after a huge lunch. The Deputy Mayor denied the allegation but it ended his political

10

career. He retired from public life in shame and lived out the rest of his life a bitter man. His last public words were, 'I lost my career because of one belch but you look at all the farts who stayed in office.'

Did you know that the zip was invented by a man who had rows of warts on both his lips? He shut his mouth one day and it zipped shut.

Belly button, fluffiest Miss Maisie Trott of Ipswich had a belly-button that produced four pounds of fluff a week at each digging. She attempted to market it as mattress stuffing, with some success at first. However her own supply of belly-button fluff dried up and she had to find it elsewhere. She began creeping into people's homes at night and stealing their belly-button fluff while they were asleep. She was eventually caught in the act and put in jail.

Blood transfusion, oddest The record for the oddest blood transfusion goes to a Mr Dracula, who came to Blackpool on holiday, was caught by the sun and fainted. He was rushed to the local hospital, where doctors and nurses were so worried over the paleness of his skin that they decided to give him a blood transfusion. Two pints of blood later, Mr Dracula made an astounding recovery. He leapt off the operating table, grabbing the remaining seven bottles of blood the doctor had ready, and vanished. Hospital staff swore they never saw him leave the hospital, nor did they ever retrieve the bottles of blood. Coincidentally, the same night a hospital porter accidentally ran a trolley over a bat that had somehow got into the hospital and was lying in a drunken stupor in the corridor. The bat was squashed flat, and the hospital closed while the local pest exterminator searched the hospital for any other unusual animal life.

Boil, largest The largest boil known was found on the neck of Doris Morris of Wapping in the 1940s. The boil was so big that Doris charged people to look at it. One day, when 'Doris boil-mania' was at its highest, seven people were gathered round her neck, watching the boil, when it burst. All seven had to be taken to hospital to have the pus scraped off. Luckily they were not seriously injured.

Breath, worst Tom Conoby of Yorkshire took great pride in having the smelliest, most rotten, most over-powering case of bad breath. Mr Conoby took up championship wrestling after being advised by a friend that it would be a suitable occupation. His friend was correct, for it is said that within ten seconds of a match beginning Conoby could knock a man unconscious simply by breathing on him. When interviewed on radio the interviewer (who was wearing a gas mask) asked him how he managed to maintain the noxious condition of his breath. Conoby replied, 'Well, I eat four bunches of garlic plus two spicy curries every day, and I clean my teeth annually.' A few years after the interview Mr Conoby died at the age of forty-seven. The doctor said his death was caused by breathing in too much of his own breath.

Bum, hairiest   The hairiest bum ever belonged to an anonymous traveller on a train between Shrewsbury and Wolverhampton in 1953. Railside observers reported to British Rail that a bearded man had his head stuck out of a window. When they checked, British Rail found that a man had gone to the lavatory to change his trousers. He had sat on the window ledge to ease them off over his ankles, whereupon the window had fallen down and trapped him, bum outwards, for all to see. He was released from his predicament by the guard at Wolverhampton.

Did you know that the highest place on earth to go to the toilet is the top of Mount Everest?

Cheeks, fattest   Humphrey Twott had the fattest, reddest face ever, combined with a very thin body. Once, standing by a pedestrian crossing, he was mistaken for a Belisha beacon by a passing motorist, who promptly crashed into him. His biggest moment of fame came when he entered the United Kingdom National Fancy Dress Competition. He went just as he was, with his mouth full of custard. When the Master of Ceremonies asked him what he was dressed as, Humphrey pressed his cheeks. The custard squelched out over the Master of Ceremonies and Humphrey announced, 'I'm a boil', and won first prize.

Dandruff, worst case of   This record goes to Mr McTosh of Scotland. Apparently everybody thought he was bald, until a doctor discovered that the flaky dry white surface on his head was actually a three-inch layer of dandruff that completely covered his hair. The doctor was unable to find an implement large enough to remove the layer of dead and rotten skin but finally achieved success by using a local stonemason's chisel. In a recent radio interview, when Mr McTosh was asked how he could possibly not have noticed the white flaky skin falling all over the place, he simply replied, 'Well, I thought it was snowing.'

Did you know that if you vomit from the top of the Empire State Building you have time to watch twenty-six episodes of Grange Hill before it hits the ground?

Ear, most swollen A South African, Edward Vlaadistart, was bitten by a snake on his left ear one day while lying in the sun. His ear swelled and swelled to such a size that it grew as big as his head. Edward tried everything to ease his earache, from soaking his head in a bucket of iced water to pricking it, but whatever he tried his ear remained huge and red and aching. His friends started to make fun of him. Edward couldn't stand this, so he painted a face on his ear, moved to a new area, and told everyone he was a pair of Siamese twins. For a few months everyone believed in Edward and Arnold Vlaadistart, especially as Edward told everyone his twin was deaf and dumb, until the swelling began to go down. People were very angry at the way they had been fooled and one man even went so far as to threaten to shoot Edward for having taken him for an idiot. Edward persuaded the man that it wasn't him but his brother Arnold who was the fraud, so the man shot him instead. Edward is now known as One-Ear Vlaadistart.

14

Ears, hairiest A Mr Harry Osborne of Wapping in London had such huge and hairy ears that insects used to seek refuge in them. These included a family of rare Chinese Tri Ful flying ants, who, arriving in England and looking for somewhere warm to nest, had chosen Mr Osborne's left ear. This gave him some problems with his hearing, and led to his condition being described as a Tri Ful deaf'.

Ears, waxiest The waxiest ears belonged to a Mr Simon Mont, whose ears produced over thirteen pounds of wax a day. With all this wax he decided to set up a candle-making factory. Mr Mont walked around with large buckets resting on his shoulders, which collected the wax that constantly oozed out of his ears. Unfortunately no one wanted to buy his candles, so he wrapped them up and sold them as soft sweet rock. This was an immediate success, and everyone commented on how wonderfully sweet the rock was when they sucked on it. Sadly Mr Mont's business packed up after one hot summer night when so much wax in his ears melted that when it hardened it turned him into a permanent waxwork.

Eyes, sleepiest A man in London woke up from a deep night's sleep and panicked when he found he could not open his eyes. His first assumption was that he had gone blind during the night, so he rushed to his doctor, having many accidents on his way. When the doctor examined the man's eyes he found that a quarter-inch-thick layer of dry, crusty sleep had covered the man's eyes, glueing the eyelids together. The doctor could not move the thick crusty layer, so he used some sandpaper to get the sleep off. Unfortunately, he accidentally sanded the man's eyelids off in the process and the man successfully sued the doctor for millions of pounds' damages.

Did you know that a cure for baldness is rubbing horse manure on your head? What happens is that no one comes near you so they can't see that you're losing your hair.

Farts, most enterprising A boy found that on a basic diet of beans he could produce over 500 noxious farts a day. These farts were exceedingly smelly and very potent. One 5th of November he was standing near a bonfire when he farted and the gas from his bum caught alight. He realized that he could make use of his noxious farts by setting up a gas factory. he tied small empty gas cylinders to his rear to catch the farts, used a machine to compress the fart gas, making it even more potent, and then put the gas into small containers. His business was very successful for some years, until he developed diarrhoea. This caused his gas cylinders to become clogged up and his customers went back to using ordinary gas.

Fart, most powerful The record for the most powerful fart belongs to a Mr Geoffrey Alderdash, who was overcome by an uncontrollable urge to fart at a rather posh party. He fought against the urge with all his might, but the powerful gas building up inside him was determined to find an outlet. Unfortunately for him, while he was in the middle of a very intellectual discussion with an attractive young lady, the fart broke out of him with such force that it rocketed him out of his chair and through the ceiling, leaving nothing but a trail of smelly gas behind him. Mr Alderdash was later found upside-down in a rubbish dump two miles away.

Feet, smelliest A man in Los Angeles, California, was desperate to do something about his very smelly feet. A friend persuaded him to seal them in polythene to prevent the smell from escaping. He followed this advice but unfortunately his feet died from lack of air and decomposed, whereupon the smell became even worse.

Did you know that if all the hedgehogs in the world were laid end to end it would be easier for cars to run them over?

Fingernails, longest The longest known fingernails belonged to the late John Pritchard, who never cut his fingernails in his life. He said that having such long fingernails did present problems. 'For instance,' he said, 'travelling on public transport is a bit of a nuisance because I'm often accidentally inflicting cuts on people when they press against my nails. What compensates for this, however, is having the ability to scratch my feet without bending down.' At the age of thirty-five Pritchard inflicted a fatal injury to himself. He was found dead with one of his thirty-three-inch nails up his right nostril; he died of internal injuries to the brain.

Did you know that if you unscrew your belly button your bum falls off?

Flat feet, saddest case of Arthur Simpson suffered from the flattest of flat feet. In an effort to cure himself he bored a hole in his left big toe and screwed in a bicycle pump. When he started to pump, however, instead of increasing the size of his feet, he unfortunately pumped all his blood back up his body to his brain, where it expanded and blew the top of his head off, splattering his brain all over the ceiling.

Food poisoning, most By mistake a lorry load of liquid manure was delivered to the kitchen of a High School in Dumfries, Scotland. The cook, who had a heavy cold and had therefore lost her senses of smell and taste, thought it was the daily delivery of custard, that day's flavour being chocolate. She added her usual quarter of a ton of sugar to the mixture, stirred it, and poured it over the apple crumble. Her cooking was so bad normally that no one noticed and it wasn't until the middle of the afternoon that the effects became evident. By 3.30 p.m. all 2000 pupils and 100 staff were in the toilets throwing up. This also stands as a record for the most amount of vomit thrown up in one place in a thirty-minute period.

Hair, filthiest A Health Visitor, inspecting the children's hair during a school visit, was horrified when she parted one boy's hair and a slug slid out. She was still reeling from the shock when a lizard that had been nestling in another clump of the boy's hair slid forward and ate the slug. On further examination, the boy's matted hair revealed three lizards, two more slugs, a snail, and a toad – all living off the nits and lice that lived on the boy's scalp. The boy claimed he'd never noticed anything unusual when he combed his hair. When asked what happened when he washed it, he replied: 'I don't need to wash it, it never gets dirty'. The Health Authority took out a court order making the boy have a skinhead haircut. They were later sued by the RSPCA for making the lizards, slugs, snail and toad homeless.

Hay fever, strangest case of Deirdre Pong suffered from terrible hay fever. She went out for a walk in a local park one hot summer day and was attacked by pollen from some suddenly blooming flowers. Immediately her nose poured snot and water so badly that within ten minutes she had lost two gallons of bodily fluid. Almost at once she dehydrated and shrank from her usual five feet four inches to one foot two inches. A friend who was with her saw what was happening and realized that unless he did something quickly Deirdre would disappear altogether. He remembered that if you put dried vegetables in water they filled out again, so he rushed and grabbed a nearby hose that the park gardeners had left. Unfortunately the water had been turned off at the mains: there was nothing he could do. Fortunately for Deirdre, a dog came along at that moment and mistook her for a twig. It cocked its leg and peed all over her and she returned to her normal size.

Itch, most painful Stefano di Moro of New Jersey, USA, was bitten by a small insect on his left elbow and developed a nasty itch. He scratched and scratched, but he could not get rid of the itch. He tried rubbing it with a stiff brush, then a wire brush, then a cheese-grater, but it still itched. His wife became worried when she saw that his left elbow was becoming sorer and sorer, and that it was always bleeding and pouring pus. She reported the matter to their doctor, who came round and said that the only way to stop Stefano scratching his elbow was to bandage it up. This didn't work however, because Stefano just tore the bandages off and carried on scratching. Soon Stefano's elbow was a mass of blood, pus, scratched bone, scabs, and exposed nerve endings. Both Stefano's wife and the doctor were worried that if things carried on this way Stefano would tear off his elbow, so they knocked him out and took him to the doctor's builder brother, who encased Stefano's left arm in a lump of concrete. This remedy was not a complete success: the next day, while he was out for a walk to take his mind off his itch, Stefano tripped and fell into a canal; the weight of the concrete caused him to sink to the bottom and he drowned.

Did you know that in some parts of the world boils are a status symbol?

Joints, loosest Ada Clogg of Little Wittering, Hampshire, is surely the owner of the loosest joints in the United Kingdom. As a girl she would dislocate her joints at the slightest provocation. On one occasion, when she was seven years old, she ran down a cobbled street and was shaken up so much that every joint in her body popped out. A passer-by picked her up and took her home in a bucket.

Knees, scabbiest A motorcycle racer, Arnoldo di Foto, was racing in the Isle of Man 'TT' races when his knee protectors slipped without his noticing. On every bend afterwards he was riding so low, as racing motorcyclists do, that he scraped his knees in the ground. Immediately a scab formed, which was knocked off on the next bend and replaced by another scab. After fifteen miles and one-hundred-and-eight bends he had achieved the record of forty-six scabs on his left knee and sixty-two on his right knee. A fan of di Foto's went along the course afterwards and collected all the scabs in a bag. The fan then proudly presented them to the motorcyclist. Di

Foto, unaware of what the fan had done, thanked him, ate one, and told him that they were the best crisps he'd ever tasted.

Lungs, largest Charlie Chuck had such big lungs that he could blow up inflatable bouncing castles at fairgrounds with one huge puff. People came from miles around to watch him perform this amazing feat. One day, just as he had nearly finished blowing up one of these enormous castles, the watching crowd accidentally fell on to it, forcing all the air to rush back into Charlie's lungs. Charlie immediately inflated and flew into the air. A hawk flying overhead was so startled by this that it pecked Charlie. All the air immediately escaped and he dropped into a sewage farm.

Laryngitis, most unusual treatment Oonagh O'Bone was in the middle of a sentence in the winter of 1959, when her voice packed up. This was not noticed by her husband, whom she was talking to at the time, as he was deaf. The next day, however, a friend noticed that her voice wasn't working when she spoke. This friend told Oonagh not to waste her time with a doctor, but to go to the local witch. The witch identified Oonagh's trouble as Rat-Throat (laryngitis) and made up a potion consisting of a pound of rotten mushrooms, a pint of water from Dublin's main sewer, a slice of dog's mess, a bucket of vomit, and a quarter of a pound of toenails. This mixture was boiled and then strained through a sieve. Oonagh drank the liquid, and the hot mess remaining was put on her throat to act as a poultice. Miraculously Oonagh recovered her voice some two months later. However, the witch's potion had some unfortunate side-effects: she was struck down later by cholera, stomach-ache, bunions, and worms.

Lungs, wheeziest Hermione Spencer, aged ninety, had the wheeziest pair of lungs ever. The kinds of sounds that she could make simply by breathing in and out were so varied that she was offered a job with the West Highlands International Bagpipe Band as lead piper, playing her lungs. In 1983, at the age of ninety-one, she won a music award for her virtuoso solo during a televized concert, in which she hit an amazing number of notes during her rendition of 'Amazing Grace'. The British Jazz Society also gave her an award for the same performance as Best Jazz Soloist of the Year. It was only later that she revealed that her 'improvisational solo' had actually been at asthma attack.

Nose-picking, richest Fred Smogg, a thirty-five-year-old blacksmith and a heavy smoker, was found to have a nose so rich in mineral deposits that the Coal Board offered to buy a share of his nostrils. A day's pickings from his nostrils, using the usual method of a forefinger up each nostril, yielded three pounds of solid black gunge with a high anthracite content. Over the course of a year Fred Smogg's nose gave over one ton of clinker. In 1983 his nose was given the Queen's Award to Industry.

Did you know that if you try to talk and spit at the same time you will suffocate?

Nose-picking, slimiest Olivera d'Olivera from Brazil had what many feel were the slimiest nostrils ever. The mucus lining his nostrils was so thick and gungy that when he picked it on one occasion a live frog came out on his finger, having made its home up there.

Skin, oiliest Doris de Souza of Plata de Manana, Brazil, had the oiliest skin ever known. As a child she was always sliding out of her mother's arms. When she went on her first date her boyfriend gave her an affectionate squeeze and she shot into the air like toothpaste from a tube. By the time she was thirty she was an embittered woman, never having been cuddled without zooming into the air at great speed, or sliding to the ground. She decided to revenge herself on the world, so she changed her name to Olive de Souza, and went around sueing for libel every person or organization that used the name olive oil. She was arrested for killing a libel lawyer, who described her as 'a slippery customer', but no prison could hold her, as she was always able to slide out between her cell bars. When last heard of she was continuing her libel tour of the world somewhere in Australia.

Sneeze, most powerful (1) The most violent sneeze ever was that of a Mr Jim McSnoosh, who lived in north Scotland. During a very nasty cold Mr McSnoosh went to sneeze, but snot had blocked up his nose completely. The large quantity of catarrh inside his nose was put under so much pressure that some of it came out through his ears. Some went upwards and caused McSnoosh serious brain damage; he died seconds later. When ambulance men arrived at his house they found the walls and ceiling spattered with green slime. Unfortunately for them they had to wade through inches of the stuff to get to the body.

Sneeze, most powerful (2)   Mavis Wilberforce caught a terrible cold in the summer of 1964. It started with the sniffles and developed into a runny nose, which dragged on for months, annoying Mavis. What Mavis wanted was a big sneeze that would blow the cold out of her system in one go. She decided the answer was to make herself sneeze, and she mixed up a powder made up of pepper, mustard, pollen, and chopped-up feathers, and stuffed it up her nose. The effect was immediate and dramatic. The cold sneeze that had been lying waiting in Mavis's nostrils was sparked into life and she sneezed with such force that she blew her nose off. It flew across the room and out through the window, killing a man walking along the street outside her house.

Stomach, noisiest Alonso O'Grady, a New York policeman, had a stomach that rumbled and bubbled so loudly that the New York Union of Plumbers protested to the City Council. They claimed that wherever O'Grady went, people heard the noise of his stomach and thought that their plumbing system was going wrong. Plumbers in O'Grady's precinct were dealing with up to one hundred false alarm calls a day. O'Grady tried various doctors but none of them could cure this noisy stomach. Deciding he could face the curse of his stomach no longer, O'Grady went to the river determined to throw himself in and end it all. However, waiting his turn in the queue of people determined to drown, he stood next to a depressed indigestion tablet manufacturer, whose business was on the verge of bankruptcy. The manufacturer heard O'Grady's stomach and realized that it was exactly the sound he had been looking for as background noise for his indigestion commercials. Immediately he offered O'Grady a job as Stomach-Rumbler. O'Grady was delighted that his life-long curse could now be a boon, and accepted. The manufacturer borrowed five million dollars for his sure-fire advertising campaign, and for the first time ever O'Grady was happy. The trouble, was this happiness caused his stomach to stop rumbling and bubbling. The poor manufacturer's campaign fell apart and he was now also five million dollars in debt. The distraught man, unable to take any more, went down to the river and threw himself in. O'Grady felt so guilty and miserable that his stomach rumblings returned even worse than before. This proves yet again that things never happen when you want them to.

Sunburn, worst Horace Smith went on holiday abroad for the first time to Spain. Not realizing how hot the sun was, or why everyone went indoors at midday, Horace went to sleep on the beach. When he woke up he was completely brick-red all down his front, from his head to his toes. Even his hair was sunburned. In fact he was so baked that as he tried to stand up, he cracked, because the skin all down his front had turned into a sort of hot cardboard. So painful was it for him to walk that he had to hop everywhere for days afterwards. A few days later, the sunburn turned into a blister, and all that could be seen of Horace was a six-foot tall bag of water made out of skin hopping about. In desperation he went to a local doctor, who jabbed the six-foot tall blister with a pin to let out all the water, and then proceeded to peel Horace's skin off like an orange. As the last flap of skin came away in the doctor's hand, Horace, without his skin to hold him together, fell apart and collapsed in a heap on the floor of the doctor's surgery.

Tapeworm, strongest A Luton mother, Ethel Crump, was horrified when her doctor told her that her son, Edgar, had a tapeworm in his bowels. The doctor gave Edgar some medicine but it did not affect the tapeworm at all. 'Obviously,' said the doctor, 'this tapeworm is extra strong and I shall have to be extra cunning in dealing with it.' So the doctor sent his nurse out for a piece of cheese, a wafer biscuit, and a hammer. The doctor put the piece of cheese on the biscuit and put the biscuit near Edgar's naked bottom. As he expected, the

tapeworm was very cunning and very quick. It popped its head out of Edgar, snatched up the cheese and biscuit, and disappeared inside Edgar before the doctor could bash it with the hammer. The second day, the doctor again put the cheese on the biscuit, and again the tapeworm was too quick and grabbed the food before the doctor could bash it. On the third day, the doctor put out just the piece of cheese. This time the tapeworm popped out, snatched the cheese and darted back into Edgar, then reappeared a second later saying, 'Where's my biscuit?' Quick as a flash the doctor hit it with the hammer, killing it.

Teeth, most deformed A man named Oscar, who lived many years ago, had two front teeth that stuck out more than two and a half feet. So embarrassed was he by these teeth that he sawed them off and sold them to an elephant tusk collector. Unfortunately the stumps he was left with made him resemble a vampire. His new next door neighbours were so frightened by him that they contracted an expert on vampires, who told them that the only answer was to bang a stake into Oscar's heart. The neighbours tried this, but unfortunately they misunderstood and used a medium-rare steak. Oscar woke up one morning and found a lump of meat lying on the top of his pyjamas. He became so worried by this that he moved out and was never seen again.

Teeth, most rotten   In New Jersey, America, in 1910, a man visited a dentist, complaining of toothache. On examination, the dentist found that the man's teeth were so rotten that each one had turned to black squidgy jelly. They were so soft that ants had burrowed into them and were using them as caves.

Did you know that the record for the furthest a cow pat has ever been thrown is fifty-seven feet for a dry one, and three inches for a wet one?

Temperature, highest   Sidney Snodgrass of Cheshire was taken ill with a fever in February 1982. That night his temperature was 100 degrees fahrenheit, and by the morning of the next day it had increased to 105. By mid-morning it had reached 109 degrees, and when the doctor called to take his tempeature in the afternoon, Sidney was so hot that the thermometer melted as soon as it was placed in his mouth. The doctor went away to fetch a temperature gauge used for measuring the heat in iron foundries but by the time he got back Sidney himself had melted. All that the doctor found of him was a heap of bones and gristle on the bed, and a pile of solidifying sweat beside it.

Toenails, dirtiest The dirtiest toenails ever reported occurred in France early this century. Surgeons were about to amputate the foot of a man, when they noticed that potatoes were growing from under his toenails. Closer examination revealed that earthworms had burrowed in and established a colony under the nail of his left big toe.

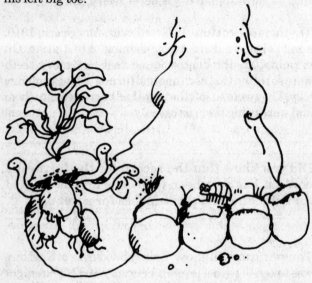

Tongue, furriest In medieval Italy, Signorina Silvania Ostra had been a strong drinker for so many years that the furo on her tongue made it resemble a white carpet. One day she looked out of her bedroom window, opened her mouth to spit, and a hawk flew down and pecked her tongue off, mistaking it for a large furry animal.

Tongue, longest The person with the longest tongue was an Indian fakir, Sjin Mij Mahir, who had lengthened his tongue by nailing it to a door and leaning backwards daily over a period of thirty-five years. By the time he was sixty-five his tongue was four feet long, and he could poke it up his nose and back out of his mouth again. While performing this ritual one day, his tongue took a wrong turning and went down his gullett, suffocating him. After his death his tongue was cut out and ritually presented to his son, who turned it into a pair of braces.

Ulcer, largest A businessman in New York who led a rather hectic and stressful life, chewed his bottom lip so much that he developed a huge two-inch-wide ulcer on the inside of his lip. The ulcer filled with blood and lasted for over a year, growing all the time, so that by the end of the year it filled his entire mouth. In fact, if a surgeon hadn't pierced the thick, rubbery surface of the ulcer with an electric drill, the man would probably have died of starvation, because he was unable to get any food into his ulcer-filled mouth. The man has recently retired from business life because he couldn't take the consequences of pressure!

Did you know that you can tell if a frog is really a prince by kissing it? If it isn't, your feet become green and webbed.

Vomit, most expensive A Mr Henry Duckworth of Oxford was invited to a very posh party by an acquaintance. When he arrived he found that the three-course meal consisted of minestrone soup, chicken stew, and blackberry pie. All these things disagreed with him but as he did not wish to offend his host and hostess, he ate the meat. Five minutes after the meal was over, Mr Duckworth's tummy rumbled and squeaked, and he vomited all over an expensive carpet, a lady's designer dress, and a £500,000 stamp collection, which his host was showing him. He was promptly sued for the replacement cost of all these items. In an interview on television about the case, Mr Duckworth said that he had never eaten out since and added, 'It was the most expensive meal I've ever had.'

Did you know that forty-seven people a year in the world are injured by hard turds falling from aeroplanes?

Warts, facial (largest) Mr Harry Potts of Wimbledon started to develop a wart on his forehead in 1975. By 1977 it had grown to a height of four inches and a width of three inches. Three years later it was so huge that Mr Potts had to wear an outsize hat to cover it. It still grew and grew, so in the end he bought a large balaclava helmet to cover his head completely whenever he went out. Unfortunately for him he then answered the description of a two-headed terrorist the security forces were looking for, and he was shot by mistake while walking across Wimbledon Common in 1983.

Yuk Quiz

1. Which animal produces the most mucus?

a) A goldfish.
b) An elephant.
c) The six-toed snortiblug.
d) I'd prefer not to know.

2. How do you get cold rice pudding off the kitchen floor?

a) With a vacuum cleaner.
b) Get the dog to eat it.
c) Eat it myself.
d) I'd definitely prefer not to know.

3. What is the best way to burst a boil?

a) Wait.
b) Sit on it.
c) Suck it (depending on where it is).
d) I'd absolutely prefer not to know.

4. What is the best way to get dog's mess off your shoe?

a) Wipe the shoe on the ground.
b) Wipe it off on someone else.
c) Lick it off.
d) How can you be so disgusting?!

5. If you fart in public do you:

a) Apologize?
b) Pretend it was someone else?
c) Smile and say, 'Thank heavens it was only a fart!'?
d) I never ever fart.

6. How do you make green?

a) Mix blue and yellow.
b) Squash a frog.
c) Eat grass and vomit.
d) I shall ignore this question.

7. Who had the biggest and hairiest nostrils?

a) Julius Caesar.
b) Attila the Hooter.
c) The Nose Transplant Department of a London Hospital.
d) My parent.

8. You fall into a tank at a sewage farm. Do you:

a) Shout for help?
b) Sink?
c) Start to drink your way out?
d) Swim, watching out for floating bits?

(For how to score *see* page 88.)

DISGUSTING HABITS

Beret, filthiest   In 1974 a beret was bought at a jumble sale in Wales that had previously belonged to someone who had never washed their hair. The beret was like stiff cardboard, and the inside was covered in a thick black solid tar from the filth and grease of the previous owner's hair. In addition, embedded in the gunge were dead lice and nits, and coating the whole mess were layers of rancid dandruff. The beret was sold for two pence.

Did you know that although a bird in the hand may be worth two in the bush, it's likely to make a mess on your fingers?

Beret, most lost   One evening a farmer was walking past one of his fields when he dimly saw a young man in the middle of it. The young man was spattered with wet and dry cow dung and, as the puzzled farmer watched, he picked up a cow pat and put it on his head. The cow pat was old and it broke into a thousand small pieces and fell inside the young man's shirt. The young man then picked up another cow pat and put that on his head. This one was fresh and the green liquidy mess in the middle of it ran down his face, and the disgusting brown mess of the rest of it slimed down the back of his

head and inside his shirt. The young man was just about to pick up another cow pat, when the farmer, who could bear it no longer, called out, 'Hey, you! What are you doing with those cow pats?!' 'I'm sorry,' said the young man, 'but the wind blew of my brown beret into this field and I'm trying to find out which one it is.'

Bib, most solid Baby Murgatroyd of Ohio, USA, has the claim to the filthiest bib ever. Trying to feed himself he missed all the time, and all the sticky food landed on his bib. This, combined with his constant dribbling and a nose that was always running with snot which slimed on to the bib, meant that the bib became as solid as concrete. Finally one day, as his mother was tying his bib on, the bib cracked down the middle and fell into little solid pieces on the table.

Coat, filthiest A tramp was found dead in an alleyway in Brooklyn, New York, in 1951. His coat was so solid with filth accumulated over the years that when it was removed it was found that no actual cloth was left. His 'coat' was made up of food stains, spittle, garbage and mess and all these had meshed into a coat shape, while the original fabric decayed and vanished. Once the 'coat' was removed from the tramp's body, it fell apart, and exists now only in a photograph taken at the time by a police photographer. The police photographer is reported to have said, 'You think the coat was bad? You should have felt inside the pocket!'

Did you know that Napoleon is always shown with his hand inside his coat because he was always scratching a pimple?

Gloves, dirtiest and most nutritious The dirtiest gloves belonged to Miss Amy Wittering, a gardener in Sussex. The gloves that she used for gardening had collected so much soil during their fifteen years of use that a small geranium had sprouted on the left palm. Some earthworms and the odd beetle also lived in the soil on the gloves, but most of all it was the quality and quantity of the plants that lived there that amazed people. It seemed that the mixture of local soil and rotting glove fabric formed a special nutritious peat-like substance that was perfect for rare plants to grow in. Miss Wittering's gloves became famous and botanists from all over the world flocked to see them. What also intrigued visitors was the fact that Miss Wittering never seemed to take off her gloves. The reason was revealed one day when she accidentally caught both her hands in the lawnmower, severing them. It was then seen that the various plants growing on the gloves had planted roots inside Miss Wittering's hands.

Hat, most rotten The dirtiest known hat belonged to a man in Scandinavia, Olaf Gustafson.Olaf's hat survived ten cold winters in which the hat had been frozen stiff. To protect his hat Olaf rubbed what he thought was leather polish on it, but unfortunately and unknown to him, Olaf had been rubbing canned dog food on his hat for the past ten years. This mistake had come about through Olaf's habit of removing the labels from tins for the coupons and competitions on them: he never really knew what was in each tin. (His dog, in the meantime, didn't look very fit, but its coat had a lovely shine to it.) The whole thing came to a head one day when Scandinavia had a very hot freak summer. Olaf's hat started to come alive as the dog food that had been frozen on it for ten years began to melt. Almost immediately it began to rot, and a sticky green mouldy fungus appeared on it. Frozen congealed blood, gristle, and marrow bone jelly thawed out and started to drip down Olaf's face and on to his shirt. Olaf's dog, smelling the rancid hat, decided he preferred it to the smell of leather polish, took a leap at Olaf and bit his head clean off, hat and all, in one bite.

Did you know that the most snot found in a handkerchief weighed one pound four ounces and was owned by the Hooter family of Wapping?

Jumper, thickest The thickest jumper was worn by a man in Scotland, Hamish McFee, whose jumper was at least five inches thick and had been made with the wool of twenty-eight Shetland sheep. The jumper was so large, covering the man from head to toe, that he was often put into sheep sales by one of the local farmers, who mistook him for a large sheep. It was because Hamish looked so like a sheep when he wore the jumper that he was finally taken to a slaughterhouse by a farmer. No matter how much Hamish protested and explained that he was not a sheep, the workers at the slaughterhouse simply presumed they had drunk too much and ignored him. Tragically they didn't discover their mistake until after they had killed him and removed his fleece. Deciding then that it was a bit too late to do anything about it, and not wanting to get into trouble, they chopped him up and added him to the next consignment of meat leaving the slaughterhouse.

Did you know that you can make yourself sick by sticking a finger down your throat, especially if you've just been picking your nose with it?

Nappies, most soiled The filthiest nappies ever were − *(This item has been censored as it is considered too disgusting even for this book. We must therefore leave it to your imagination − that's how bad it is.)*

Pyjamas, baggiest and most elastic The largest and most elasticated pair of pyjamas were worn by a man in London, Oscar Brownloaf. Oscar's pyjamas fitted him perfectly when he bought them but over the years the elastic in them stretched so much that the pyjamas became at least four times Oscar's size. One night he woke to find that the pyjamas were so large that they had slipped over his bed and his bed was actually inside his pyjamas. While sleeping one night by the open window, Oscar rolled out of his bed and fell straight out of the window. Fortunately his pyjamas caught on a nail and the elastic stretched to its maximum just before Oscar hit the ground. Less fortunate, however, was the fact that before Oscar knew where he was, the elastic was pulling him back again, catapulting him into the air. He went up into the air with such force that, as he whizzed through some overhead telegraph wires, he was shredded. He was later found in strips all over the pavement. The pyjamas, however, were intact, albeit rather larger.

Did you know that if you fart in outer space no one can hear it?

Did you know that you can catch dandruff? Just shake your head over a cardboard box!

Shawl, tattiest   The tattiest known shawl was worn by an old Scottish lady, Fiona McPudden. The garment wasn't actually a shawl but a carpet that a Health Inspector had told her was so unhygienic that it must be removed from the house. Fiona hated to part with anything, so she said it was a family heirloom and refused to dispose of it. To get around the problem with the Health Inspector, she took to wearing it as a shawl. Unfortunately, as the garment was so tatty and stank to high heaven, when people saw her approaching many passed out. The smell was the worst thing about the shawl, as, during its time as a carpet, several of Fiona's pets had messed on it and she hadn't bothered to clean it afterwards. Nor had she bothered to clean it after her cat had been sick on it, her Grandmother had haemorrhaged on it, her dog had killed two rats on it and ground their insides into it. Also sticking to the shawl were the remains of her two husbands, whom Fiona had murdered and chopped up on it when it had been a carpet. As Fiona said, 'My whole life is in that shawl.'

Shirt, sweatiest Edgar Foot, a marathon runner, is thought to hold this record. After running the London marathon in 1984, it was noticed that his T-shirt seemed to have a layer of glistening oil coated on it. In fact, it was completely drenched in sweat. Edgar's body was well known for its ability to produce large amounts of sweat but in this case he had excelled himself. The shirt was so saturated that it had already begun to harden with solidifying sweat and Edgar's friends had to scrape the hardening sweat off the outside of the shirt before Edgar could even move properly. They scraped off twenty-eight pounds of grease and sweaty, stinking gunge. Edgar was then able to remove his shirt and wring it out, producing a further one-and-a-half gallons of slimy sweat.

Did you know that it is unlucky to spit into the wind? (The wind blows it back and it dribbles down your front.)

Slippers, stickiest Gerald Carlisle of Edinburgh had the stickiest slippers ever, This was because he never washed the floor of his kitchen and splashed frying fat and spilled food formed a congealing layer over the floor. This led to Gerald's slippers becoming so sticky that one day they set hard to the floor of his hallway as he went to answer his doorbell. This caused Gerald to fall over and knock himself out against his front door.

Did you know that if everyone faced the sun and belched at the same time, the earth would go out of its orbit?

Did you know that if you bite your fingernails and swallow them they grow into fingers inside you?

Socks, hardest The hardest known socks belonged to a Canadian in Montreal, who wore these particular woolly socks nearly every day for three years. The sweat from the man's feet would saturate his socks, mix with dust, dirt and grime, and then dry to form a stiff glue, making the socks rock hard. One night there was a power cut at the man's home and, as he was stumbling around his house in the dark in his socks, he accidentally stubbed his foot against a table leg, shattering the table instantly. Inspired by this, the man got a job in the demolition business, simply kicking walls down with his feet, wearing only his super-hard socks. He was forced to retire from the business when he forgot to put his socks on one day. He kicked a wall and broke every bone in his foot.

Did you know that in Australia when they dribble it goes *up* their face from their mouths and runs into their hair?

Socks, most deadly   During the Second World War an army commander, General Ponsby, received complaints from his officers that one of their own soldiers was causing major casualties in the barracks with the smell from his socks. This smell was so bad that a whole barracks-full of soldiers who shared with this soldier, Private Hedge, had been invalided as unfit. The smell was described as like that from a thousand dead rats, the worst fart in the world, and a thousand decaying maggots, all rolled into one. A sergeant, on bending down to inspect the shine on Private Hedge's boots, had been overcome by the noxious fumes and had dropped dead on the spot from gas poisoning. General Ponsby, instead of dismissing the Private from the Army, saw this as a great opportunity to win the war. He decided to have all the smelly, rotten and decomposing socks that had been worn by Private Hedge wrapped around shells and fired from the guns of his tanks. Unfortunately for General Ponsby and his men, this brilliant scheme backfired, because the lethal gas penetrated the gas masks that this men wore, killing them first. After more than 500 of the General's men died due to gas poisoning, a military scientist examined the gas and decided to call it Sockthane. The scientist also said that the gas would have been far more useful if it had been discovered during the First World War, rather than the Second.

Taxi customer, worst   Late one night a Bristol taxi driver, Morris Morris, picked up a customer. The man got into his cab loaded down with parcels. They had only been travelling a little while when the customer said to Morris, 'Excuse me, do you have room beside you in the front for a pizza and ten pints of beer?' 'Certainly,' replied Morris, eager to help. So the customer leant forward and vomited all over the empty front seat.

Did you know that a Manx cat has three legs and no tail? This was proved when such a cat was found in a lawnmower on the Isle of Man.

Did you know that royalty have servants who belch for them after a heavy meal?

Thermal underwear, hottest   In the summer of 1976 a man in Somerset, Samuel Smiles, misheard the weather forecast and thought that it would be freezing cold the next day. So the next morning he heaped on all his thermal underwear, plus a thick woolly jumper on top. However, when Samuel went out to do his shopping he found that it was actually baking hot. Deciding it wasn't worth going home to change, Samuel continued with his shopping. After he had been out for about an hour, Samuel suddenly collapsed in the street, unconscious. An ambulance was called and Samuel was taken to the hospital. When the nurses removed Samuel's clothes, they found that he had become so hot that all his body fat had melted down into a liquified gunge, which oozed out through the pores of his skin. When they weighed the congealed globs of glistening fat they calculated that Samuel had lost six stones in

47

weight. The temperature inside his thermal underwear had reached 120 degrees centigrade, and if his clothes had been removed any later poor Samuel's body fat would have dissolved completely and he would have been literally roasted alive inside his thermal underwear.

Tie, most food-stained   A Mr Montague Merlin of Shropshire had only one tie, which he wore every day. Unfortunately he was a very messy eater and his tie became covered in bits of food from all his meals. While Mr Merlin was picnicking one summer, a fly flew by and

laid its eggs in the blobs of food hanging from his tie. When the eggs hatched out, the maggots crawled up the tie and started to eat their way through the skin and flesh of Mr Merlin's chin and up into his mouth. Poor Mr Merlin thought it was just cramp in his jaw, and he didn't realize the awful truth until the maggots started to eat their way through his brain.

Did you know that in some parts of the world picking pimples is a martial art?

Waiter, most disgusting Edgar Small was in a restaurant in Birmingham and he noticed that the waiter who brought him his soup had his thumb well and truly in it. Mr Small didn't like complaining but he felt he had to say something, so he said to the waiter, 'Your thumb is in my soup.' The waiter apologized and Mr Small thought that was the end of the matter. However, when the waiter brought him his next course, Mr Small noticed that the waiter's thumb was well and truly in the gravy. Again Mr Small complained, and again the waiter apologized, and again Mr Small thought that was the end of the matter. However, when the waiter brought Mr Small his pudding, his thumb was well and truly in the custard. This was too much for Mr Small and he really lost his temper. The waiter, very apologetic, explained that he had sprained his thumb and the doctor had told him to keep it somewhere warm and moist. 'I couldn't care about your thumb!' stormed the angry Mr Small. 'As far an I'm concerned you can stick it up your bum.' 'Yes,' said the waiter, 'that's where I keep it when it's not in the food.'

Yuk Quiz

9. Which food is the most disgusting?

a) A cat food and jelly sandwich.
b) Stewed tarantula and chips.
c) A hot dog (made from real dog)
d) Semolina pudding.

10. Which animal can stay under water longest without breathing?

a) A goldfish.
b) A shark.
c) A turtle.
d) A dead cat.

11. What do you do if you find an insect in your food at a restaurant?

a) Complain.
b) Eat it and say nothing.
c) Put it on someone else's plate.
d) Eat it and order another.

12. Which has the worst breath?

a) A snail.
b) A human being.
c) The lesser-spotted turd-eater.
d) I don't want to know.

13. **If you see that the person you're talking to has a large bogey hanging from their nose, do you:**

a) Tell them?
b) Pick it off?
c) Go and talk to someone else?
d) Faint?

14. **If a butcher gets a little behind in his orders, does it mean:**

a) He's late with his work?
b) He's caught his bum in his bacon slicer?
c) Someone else caught their bum in his bacon slicer?
d) I intend to prosecute the authors of this book?

15. **If your teeth start to fall out, what is the best thing for keeping them in?**

a) Gum gum.
b) A dentist.
c) A paper bag.
d) I suppose you think that's funny.

16. **What is the difference between head lice and nits?**

a) One half-inch.
b) Nits are just stupid head lice.
c) Head lice are crunchier when you eat them.
d) I have never had either and nor has anyone I know.

(For how to score *see* page 88.)

CREEPY CRAWLIES

Bedbugs, most squashed A tourist in India was about to go to bed one night when he noticed that his white bed sheet was black. He presumed that the maid had changed the sheets during the day, and got into bed. Once in bed, he heard a loud crunching sound underneath him. He leapt out of bed immediately, and to his horror found loads of crunched, squashed and half-dead bedbugs, with their insides oozing out of them, all over his back. He had a shower and eventually managed to scrape off the bedbug remains from his back and the sheets. It was then that he realized that the sheets were not black at all but had only looked it because of the thousands of bedbugs that were crawling all over them. The sheets were now stained yellow-brown from the insides of the bedbugs. During the night the bedbugs got their own back when their dad came along and tipped the man out of bed. The man was so scared at waking up to find a giant bedbug in his bed that he left the hotel. The bedbugs were later evicted for not paying their bill.

Caterpillar, largest and most delicious Recently a vegetarian went into a very expensive restaurant in America and asked for some fresh vegetable soup. The chef went out into the garden at the back of the restaurant and picked some fresh cabbage and other vegetables. When the soup arrived, the vegetarian complained that there were huge six-inch-long boiled caterpillars in his soup and that as far as he knew caterpillars were not vegetables. The chef disagreed that they were caterpillars and claimed that they were the stems of plants. To prove his point, the chef picked one out of the soup and bit it in half. Out of the chef's mouth dribbled the boiled innards of the caterpillar: guts, pus, and the contents of the caterpillar's stomach. The chef choked and fainted, and the customer got a refund.

Cockroaches, biggest The slums of New York are reckoned to house the biggest cockroaches in the world. The tenant of one of these slums described how he and his family had been woken one night by an unusual crunching sound, and had found a pack of cockroaches eating the walls of their apartment. 'They were enormous,' said the man, 'about four feet tall. Granny grabbed a broom and tried to squash them but one of the cockroaches just scooped her up and ate her. It was terrible, particularly because she was wearing her new nightdress. The only good thing to come out of it was that the landlord came to collect the rent the next day the cockroaches ate him. They must have been tough to eat that character.'

Fleas, most on an animal A cat in Mexico had so many fleas that it wasn't until four days after it died that people realized that it was dead. Its owner reported seeing the cat move from the living room to the kitchen two days after it died. He said, 'I thought its fur felt a bit odd when I stroked it as it passed me, but you know what cats are like.'

Did you know that the largest tapeworm was three feet two inches long and was called Albert?

Fleas, strongest A Mr Pickleworth of Bognor was thought to be the person with the most fleas. Pickleworth had a pair of woollen socks that he wore all the time, even in bed. When he bought the socks they were white, but after a few days so many fleas inhabited them that the socks turned a blackish, fleaish colour. The socks made an ideal home for the fleas because when they were hungry they could suck as much blood as they wanted from Pickleworth, and when they wanted to sleep they had the nice, cosy woollen socks to keep them warm. Sometimes if the fleas all jumped at once they lifted Pickleworth's feet off the ground a few inches. The fleas practised this trick and got better and better at it until they were able to lift him up and make him jump like a flea. It was this trick that was the end of Pickleworth and the fleas because, on a sightseeing tour of the Grand Canyon in America, while standing on the edge of the Canyon, Pickleworth suddenly did a large flea-like jump forward off the edge.

Did you know that a three-legged dog can't pee against a tree without falling over?

Fly, largest A macabre discovery was made in Birmingham in 1937. People complained to the police of unusual sounds and a very sickly smell coming from an empty house in a run-down part of Birmingham. There were also reports of people and animals going missing in the area, so the police broke into the house and found that a huge fly had set up its nest there. The fly was at least two feet across, and such was its appetite that it had been going out into Birmingham at night, killing people and animals, and bringing them back to its nest to eat. The smell came from the fly's decomposing 'larder'. The police killed the fly and donated its carcass to the Birmingham Natural History Museum.

Head lice, worst case of   Louis IX of France holds this
revolting record. It all started when people were amazed
that, at the age of thirty-three, his hair had turned grey.
His friends urged him to consult the court physician.
When the court physician came to examine a strand of
Louis' hair he found that it was not grey at all, but that
millions of grey head lice were covering the strand. On
closer examination, the physician found that near the
scalp they had burrowed down so deeply that there was
no skin left at all, and in places the skull had been gnaw-
ed away by the little creatures. 'In fact,' the court physician told Louis, 'if they had been allowed to inhabit your
head for just one week longer, they would have burrowed into your brain.'

Maggots, most in an apple   The most maggots found
in an apple were discovered by an apple farmer in 1974
in Somerset. The farmer was trying out a new form of
organic farming that used huge amounts of rotting fruit
as fertilizer. This led to a plague of maggots inside every
one of his apples, which he discovered only when he picked one of his new shiny apples off one of his trees and
took a bite. He found that the apple inside the skin was
composed entirely of maggots. Unfortunately for him
he only spotted this when he took his second bite. On
his first bite he had mistaken the white writhing mass
inside the apple as particularly crunchy and juicy apple
flesh.

Mussel, most deaths caused by   A man who lived in Pennsylvania had only one eye. One evening, when he was going to an important social function, his glass eye fell out, rolled into the gutter, and fell down a drain. The man was horrified: it was too late to get a replacement eye, and a marble from a toy shop would be the wrong shape. Then he saw a fish shop across the road that was selling fish eyes. The man paid for a fish eye and made a grab for one. Unfortunately, with his one good eye not working properly, the man dipped his hand in the wrong tray and picked up a live frozen mussel, which he stuffed into his empty eye socket. All went well at the social gathering at first, until the heat of the evening made the mussel thaw out. The man felt something wet on his cheek, and the next second the people around him started to faint as they saw what they thought was his eye crawl out of his eye socket and begin to slide down his cheek. In the ensuing stampede away from him, seven people were trampled to death. The headline in the paper next day read: 'Man with an eye for trouble.'

Did you know that a mosquito's left ear is bigger than its right one?

Parasites, human, most bizarre   In 1891 a man named Bert Hepplewhite collapsed in a street in Manchester and was taken to a local doctor. When the doctor removed Mr Hepplewhite's clothing he found that the whole of his patient's body was covered in leeches, busily slurping Mr Hepplewhite's blood. When asked how this had come about, Mr Hepplewhite said that his job was breeding leeches and he had been taking them for an outing.

Slug, largest and squidgiest Mr Davies Jones, who lived in a rather derelict old cottage, is known to have seen this record-breaking slug. One night, while Mr Jones was asleep, a huge fat squidgy slug, reckoned to be about a foot long and three inches wide, crawled in through his bedroom window. It then slithered to the foot of Mr Jones's bed and dozed off. The next morning Mr Jones woke up, stepped out of bed and on to the huge slug, squashing it, slipped, and went head first out of his bedroom window. Owing to the speed with which he travelled from his bedroom window, Mr Jones broke his neck on the pavement and died instantly. Later, an ambulance came to take away Mr Jones's body, and the remains of the slug that had been squashed like a brown jelly over the bedroom floor. The rest of the slug and its innards were found stuck to Mr Jones's foot.

Did you know that the thing that's worse than finding a maggot in an apple after you've taken a bite at it, is finding half a maggot?

Did you know that in the jungles of Africa baby apes born without knees can get two ape-knees for one penny?

Spiders, largest   The largest, fattest, hairiest spider was discovered by Colonel Gartfast in his attic in Africa. The attic had not been inhabited for eighty years when the Colonel went up there to get some privacy. He sat down on what he thought was a large, eight-legged stool. As he put his weight on it a mixture of slime and yellow pus oozed out of the spider's mouth. The spider was so big that when the zoo came to take it away they could not get it out of the house and they were forced to kill the poor creature. Six four-inch-long hairs about the size of nails were found by a doctor in the Colonel's bum.

Toad, fattest   The fattest toad, measuring 40 inches round the middle, was originally the thinnest toad. He was the pet of a young boy in Missouri, USA, who was worried that his pet might feel inferior at being so thin. To prevent this the boy, Gary, took his toad down to the local garage to give him a quick puff of air from the air-pump to inflate him a little. Unfortunately the toad blew up too fast too soon, and before Gary could shut the air off, his pet toad, who had blown up like a balloon, exploded. Gary's toad was therefore the fattest ever for .001 of a second.

Toad, flattest A man went swimming in a lake in Louisiana. Afterwards, he returned to his clothes and put them on without noticing that a large, fat, slimy toad had crawled inside his shirt. As the man walked back to his car he felt something wet and slimy slithering down his back and into the seat of his trousers, but he had dried himself very quickly and he thought it was just a trickle of water. It wasn't until he got into his car and squashed the toad flat inside the seat of his trousers and felt the clammy, squishy innards ooze down his trouser leg that he realized what had happened.

Did you know that Jupiter is made of pus?

Wood lice, most protected　A 250-year-old oak tree that had been planted by King George II in Hertfordshire was being visited by one of George II's descendants when the tree collapsed, nearly killing the poor chap. However, when the tree hit the ground there was nothing to be seen except a large pile of rotten sawdust, among which were millions of wood lice munching away at the remains of the wood. There was, in fact, such a large colony of wood lice that the Chairman of the local Wildlife Trust, who said that wood lice were becoming extinct, had the remains of the tree protected for the second time. It is thought that the remains of the tree will provide food for the colony of wood lice for another 250 years.

Worms, most in vomit　One day a man in Brighton accidentally swallowed a worm. The worm laid its eggs in the man's stomach and soon a whole host of worms hatched out and started to slither and slide around in the man's stomach. They started to travel further afield, some going down into the man's bowels, but most venturing into the man's gullet. All the man knew was that he started to feel sick. He ran upstairs to his bathroom, put his head over the washbasin, and retched. The next

second, whole mouthfuls of wriggling worms spewed out of his mouth and into the washbasin. Eventually the washbasin was half-filled with wriggling, writhing worms. There were so many that the man was unable to wash them down the plug hole.

Yuk Quiz

17. Which ruler had the smelliest armpits?

a) King Henry VIII.
b) Queen Boadicea.
c) King Kong.
d) This question insults royalty.

18. Which is the most dangerous to health?

a) Dirty fingernails.
b) Cat's hairs in soup.
c) Bubonic plague.
d) Teachers.

19. What is the difference between tripe and onions and a bucket of sick?

a) Tripe and onions are saltier.
b) You can't eat a bucket of sick with a fork.
c) No difference.
d) I absolutely definitely don't want to know.

20. How can you tell if a dog has fleas?

a) It says, 'I have fleas, woof woof.'
b) It scratches.
c) It keeps moving around the room when it is asleep.
d) What is a flea?

21. Which famous artist kept a live ferret down his trousers?

a) Van Gogh.
b) Leonardo da Vinci.
c) Picasso.
d) Charlie 'No knees' Hoskins.

22. A flying bird drops its mess on your head. What do you do?

a) Pretend it's dandruff.
b) Think: It's lucky that cows can't fly.
c) Stay there and hope it happens again.
d) Ignore it.

23. How can you tell if you've got a tapeworm?

a) You always feel hungry.
b) A long white thing pokes its head out of your bum.
c) Something drinks your glass of water in the night while you're asleep.
d) I do not know what a tapeworm is.

24. Which food causes diarrhoea most often?

a) Prunes.
b) Prunes, prunes, prunes and more prunes.
c) Food eaten from a dustbin.
d) School meals.

(For how to score *see* page 88.)

REVOLTING FOOD

Breakfast cereal, most insects in A health fanatic, Mr Edgar Plod of Whitstable, used to buy his muesli breakfast cereal, a mixture of dried fruit, nuts and cereal, in huge sacks and store them in a cupboard in his kitchen. This way he saved money. However, because the sacks stayed in his cupboard for such a long time, insects burrowed their way in and nested inside the

muesli. These included centipedes, millipedes, beetles, ants, lice, cockroaches, fleas, and silverfish. As time went by these insects bred larger and larger families, feeding on the muesli all the time. One day Mr Plod poured himself a bowl of his favourite breakfast cereal and poured milk over it. He was halfway through his second mouthful when he noticed that it was nearly ninety per cent insects, and he had already eaten a spoonful of millipedes and cockroaches.

Café, most disgusting crockery in A café in Somerset had a sign that said 'Chips with everything.' One customer remarked that the sign referred to the chips and cracks in the crockery. One plate had such a long deep crack in it that it was a wonder the plate held together. As the plates were only ever lightly washed, this long crack in this particular plate had, over the years, become filled with egg and bacon grease, oil, coagulated fat, ketchup and other sauces, and the putrefying remains of boiled vegetables, and was now a dark, gungy mess in which germs and bacteria were breeding. This gunge was so rancid that the germs and microbes breeding in it became ultra-strong, and started to creep out from the crack on to the plate whenever a meal was served on it. One customer was shocked to see the sausage on his plate disappear as the bacteria crept out of the crack and devoured it. Another customer using the same plate a short while later watched in horror as the germs crept out of the crack in a frothing, gungy mass and ate his whole meal, including the bone of the chop he had been about to gnaw.

Chips, worst A monastery in Heartfordshire was running out of money, so to raise funds it opened a fish and chip shop in a nearby town. After some complaints about the quality of the fish and chips, a Health Inspector was called in and bought a portion of cod and chips. Although the cod tasted all right, the chips were disgusting: one chip had a whole eye squashed inside it. The Health Inspector called the monk behind the counter over and complained vigorously.

'That's nothing to do with me,' said the monk.

'Why not?' asked the outraged Health Inspector.

'Because I'm just the fish friar'.

'Then who is to blame?' demanded the Health Inspector.

'Easy, that's Father Albert and Father Fred.'

'Why are they responsible?' asked the Health Inspector.

'Because,' said the fish friar, 'they're the chip monks.'

Did you know that if you eat alphabet soup you can send messages by farting?

Curry, hottest A Yorkshireman, Harvey Wallaby, went into a restaurant while visiting London and ordered a curry. The curry was so hot that the first mouthful set fire to his tongue, the second caused his eyeballs to be singed, and the third blew his head clean off his neck in a huge explosion. The owner of the restaurant said at the inquest, 'It taught us a lesson. Now we insist on customers paying their bill before they eat their meal.'

Drink, most disgusting A man in a pub in Warwickshire boasted that he could drink anything. The other people in the pub were so fed up with his boasting that one of them blew a noseful of snot into a pint glass and offered it to the boaster. 'Here,' he said 'drink this.'

The boaster looked a bit sick but, as everyone was watching him, he took the glass and started to gulp down its contents. He completely emptied the glass.

'Ugh,' said the man who had challenged him. 'You made your point with the first sip, there was no need to drink it all.'

'I didn't have any choice,' said the boaster. 'It was all in one lump.'

Food additives, most in food   A survey of additives in food found that a packet of custard powder in a supermarket in Oswestry contained only additives and no original foods at all. Amongst the 127 additives found were:

E1032 – lead
E1045 – coal tar
E1109 – hydrochloric acid
E1214 – a pair of old boots
E1347 – the toenail clippings of a mouse suffering from mange
E1408 – a bucket of vomit from a hospital for tropical diseases
E1555 – dandruff from a scabby cat.
E1628 – a variety of dog turds from a veterinary hospital specializing in animal constipation
E1776 – colouring

Jam, stickiest   The stickiest jam known was served up for breakfast at a boarding house in Lancashire. It was alleged to be raspberry jam. One of the guests tried to put some on his toast but his knife stuck in the jam and wouldn't budge. Eventually, with the aid of a spoon and a shovel, he was able to get some of the jam out of the jar and on to his toast. Unfortunately, when he bit into the toast, the jam stuck his teeth together permanently, and forever afterwards he had to be fed through a tube drilled into his neck just below his ear.

Did you know that boiled eggs cause constipation and prunes cause diarrhoea? So what would happen if you ate a boiled egg and prune sandwich?

Jelly, wobbliest The wobbliest jelly ever was discovered in Brighton. It was eaten by a man in a seaside tea room. Being a greedy man, he ate the whole jelly. The jelly was so wobbly that it shook from side to side inside his stomach as he walked along the promenade. With one particularly violent wobble it threw him off the pavement and into the path of an oncoming bus. In hospital afterwards, with every bone in his body broken, he remembered too late what his mother had always told him, that eating too much jelly is bad for your health.

Loaf, most mould on The mouldiest loaf ever was discovered in the back of a cupboard in Birmingham. The tenant of the flat died some months earlier, and neighbours were investigating peculiar scurrying sounds coming from the flat when they found the loaf. At first they didn't recognize it as it was completely covered with living fungus, originally green and furry, but now white and rancid as it burst like a mass of boils on a crust of green mould. Mushrooms and toadstools had started to sprout on it, and at least four unidentifiable but slimy insects had burrowed into the putrid loaf to set up home. As one of the neighbours was about to spray disinfectant into the cupboard, the loaf suddenly leapt out at him, and tore a hole in his throat, then it dropped to the floor, rushed out through the door, and was never seen again.

Meal, most digested   Jason Jones of Sunderland was well known as the worst glutton in a family of gluttons and at meal times he always tried to eat more than his fair share of food. The rest of the family objected to his greediness, so one dinner-time, before anyone else had arrived, he went into the kitchen, where the table was already laid for dinner. He took the lid off the casserole dish and ate four ladlesful of stew. Unfortunately the stew was terrible: the meat was so 'off' that the stew had maggots floating in it. Jason vomited it all up on one of the plates laid out for dinner and then went off to find something to drink to take away the taste. While he was out, his sister Tabitha came into the kitchen, saw the stew on the plate, and ate it. Like Jason, she spewed it back up on the plate. Four other members of the Jones family came in after her, and each ate the contents of the plate, vomiting it up afterwards. What was interesting was that each time they vomited it, they left more on the plate than had been there before. The last person to eat it, Granny Jones, was made so sick by it, that she never made it back to the table, vomiting on the floor, where the family dog ate it all. The family dog then went outside where it died of vomit poisoning.

Did you know that the record for eating the most live centipedes in one go is held by a man in Birmingham?

Meal, unhappiest   A lady from Surrey, Mrs Miranda Wix, went into a restaurant while on holiday in the Philippines, taking her beloved pet poodle, Bonzo, with her. The waiter gestured questioningly at the dog, and Mrs Wix guessed that he was making a point about hygiene and offering to take care of the dog while she was having her meal. She nodded and handed her dog's lead to the waiter, who disappeared with Bonzo. Her meal arrived, a local recipe, and it was delicious. She wanted to compliment the chef on the food, and she asked another customer if he would translate for her. He said he would, and it was during Mrs Wix's conversation with the chef and the waiter that she found out that she had eaten Bonzo; the waiter had been under the impression that she'd brought the dog in for them to cook.

Did you know that a woman in Cardiff holds two world records: 1) for eating the most prunes at one go; 2) for the longest ever time spent on a lavatory in one sitting?

Monkey brains, raw The Snodgrass family spent some time in the Far East in the early part of the twentieth century. By the time they returned to their home in Yorkshire they had developed a taste for the Eastern dish of raw monkey brains, eaten straight from the monkey's sliced-open skull. Monkeys were in short supply in Yorkshire but they made an arrangement with the local zoo to buy any surplus monkeys as 'family pets'. This disgusting favourite dish lost favour one meal-time, when Mrs Snodgrass dropped her monkey's head under the table before she could slice it open. Mr Snodgrass, always the perfect gentleman, crawled under the table to pick it up. As the monkey's head had rolled, Mr Snodgrass couldn't immediately find it, so he popped his head up beside his wife to ask in which direction it had gone. His wife, thinking it was the monkey's head

being offered to her by Mr Snodgrass (Mr Snodgrass was
a very hairy and ugly man), sliced off the top of her husband's head. She was halfway through eating his brain,
when their son Fred spotted the monkey's head lying
under a chair. The Snodgrass family never ate raw
monkey brains again.

Mushrooms, slimiest Deirdre Dollop of Norwich
was addicted to mushrooms; she ate them for nearly
every meal. Because they were so expensive she decided
to grow her own in her cellar. However, what she
did not realize was that at night her cellar was
infested with slugs and snails that left slimy trails over
everything including the mushrooms. Never having
seen mushrooms grow before, Deirdre assumed that
mushrooms were always slimy at first. Being into
'natural foods', Deirdre also decided that washing home-
grown food washed away all the natural goodness and
decided that the sliminess was part of the natural
goodness. The sliminess gave her mushrooms a par-

ticularly odd taste: sticky and greasy but nutty, too. It was after she had been eating her cellar-grown mushrooms for two weeks that Deirdre was taken ill. She went to her doctor, who diagnosed snail-enteritis and slug-rot. She also had twelve million snail and slug eggs growing inside her. Before the eggs could spawn the doctor took a major decision and sent Deirdre to the vet with a note for the chief vet. Acting on the instructions in the note, the vet put Deirdre down.

Pickled onion, sharpest A boy went into a fish and chip shop in Carlisle and bought a pickled onion. As soon as he was outside the shop he bit into it. The pickled onion was so full of vinegar and acid that it curdled the boy on the spot. First his mouth wrinkled up and shrivelled, then the rest of his head, then − as the fumes and sharp acidy flavour from the pickled onion worked their way through his taste buds to the rest of his body − the rest of him shrivelled up. He was found the next day on the pavement by a passer-by: a perfectly shrunken embalmed human being, just six inches tall. When the investigating police officer asked his mother the name of his doctor, she replied, 'Which doctor?'

'Ah,' said the police officer, 'that explains it.'

Pie, most odd During the American War of Independence in 1776 a lone British soldier was lost in the backwoods of Massachusetts. He came upon a small town and went into a small, rough tavern. He was recognized as a British soldier immediately and five local men jumped up, pulled out their guns, and ordered him to put his hands up. Before they could fire, the British soldier amazed everyone with his speed by picking up a wooden bench and knocking the five men out. The British soldier then went up to the bar and bought a pie. He took the crust off the pie, then went back to the five unconscious men, cut off their ears, stuffed them into the pie, and ate it. The other locals were horrified by this brutality.

'That was terrible!' thundered one outraged woman. 'What regiment are you with?'

'I'd have though that was obvious,' said the British soldier. 'I'm with the Pioneer (pie-and-ear) Corps.'

Did you know that tapioca looks exactly the same as frog spawn?

Porridge, lumpiest A hotel in Eastbourne accidentally served up wallpaper paste instead of porridge due to a confusion over similar looking packets. The hotel guests assumed that the porridge was lumpier than usual and ate it all up. It was afterwards, when they were drinking their tea, that the trouble started: the tea mixed with the wallpaper paste in their stomachs and expanded to such a degree that all the guests became bloated and then burst, splattering bones, livers, lungs, bowels, stomachs, and wallpaper paste everywhere. Meanwhile, the wallpaper that the decorators had put up in the hall of the hotel fell off the walls as the porridge dried.

Restaurant, filthiest kitchen A plush restaurant in the West End of London, Les Jambes de l'Escargot, is the surprising holder of the record for the filthiest kitchen restaurant. A surprise visit by Public Health officials revealed the following: a two-inch-thick layer of grease and fat over everything, including the floor, walls, and ceilings; dead rats in the soup tureens; a chef, who suffered from constant diarrhoea, and never washed his hands before handling food; penicillin growing on every piece of meat; worms in all the vegetables; fungus growing on dried and congealed blood on all kitchen utensils; and a dead and decomposing ex-customer in the fridge, his corpse containing a family of mice eating his entrails. The owner of the restaurant said in court, 'We've never had any complaints before.'

Did you know that factories employ worms to push toothpaste into the tubes?

Salad, most unfortunate A Mr Frederick Robertson was at a buffet luncheon, trying to impress his boss's wife, Mrs Eve Sprout, while eating a salad. Suddenly his teenage son, John, appeared and muttered urgently, 'Dad, Dad!' But Frederick just glared at him, whispered to him to go away, and continued trying to impress Mrs Sprout. Two minutes later his son returned and whispered even more urgently, 'Dad, Dad!' This time Frederick angrily ordered John to go away and told him he'd see him later.

After he had finished entertaining Mrs Sprout, Frederick sought out John and demanded, 'What on earth did you mean by interrupting me like that!?'

'It doesn't matter now,' said John. 'I was going to tell

you that there was a great big fat slug stuck underneath your lettuce, but you've eaten it now.'

Did you know that lumpy gravy is a sign that the cook has a cold?

Sandwiches, worst A sandwich bar opened in central London advertising itself as selling 'The Newest In Fast Food – Exotic Mystery Sandwiches'. The sandwich bar did a roaring trade, until one day a newspaper reporter investigated what was inside the 'mystery sandwiches', and found the following fillings:

crushed lice paté
jellied dogs' hairs

chocolate spread made of scrapings from the soles
of shoes

jam made from ground-up hamsters

squashed hedgehog 'peanut butter'

sawdust and garlic spread

congealed socks

rats' tails in jelly

cold custard and worms with pickle

The sandwich bar closed the next day.

Spaghetti, most mobile A worm trainer was walking down a street in Manchester when he tripped and fell and his suitcase, containing his mass of performing earthworms, fell open. The worms, seeing a chance of freedom, slipped through the nearest door, which happened to lead to the kitchen of a restaurant. Inside the kitchen, a short-sighted waiter on his way to a customer with a plate of spaghetti bolognese, dropped the spaghetti right beside the mass of worms. The waiter scraped the whole lot, worms and all, off the floor and on to the plate and took it into the restaurant to the customer. The customer took three mouthfuls before he became aware that some of his spaghetti was moving, and in fact was leaving the plate and making for the edge of the table. The customer screamed and fainted, at which some of the worms he had eaten were able to slide back up his throat and out of his mouth, and head for the door. Another customer, seeing all this, was heard to say, 'And I was going to complain because there was a fly in my soup!'

84

Wine, worst A man from Rochester in Kent, Adrian Phartwater, regularly came into his local wine bar and was always boring the other customers with his knowledge of wine. 'I am a real connoisseur,' he said. 'I can recognize any wine from anywhere in the world just by drinking one glass.'

The other customers tested him with the most unusual wines but Adrian always guessed them correctly. One man was particularly fed up with Adrian, and one night he took an empty, unlabelled wine bottle from behind the bar and went outside. He came back shortly afterwards and gave the bottle, now full, to Adrian.

'Name this one,' he challenged.

Adrian poured out a glass and drank it down. Then his expression changed to one of disgust and he started to spit.

'Ugh!' he screamed. 'It's pee!'

'Yes,' said the man, 'but whose?'

Yuk Quiz

25. How can you tell if a cat has been to the toilet in your garden?

a) A turned-over pile of earth.
b) It's stuck to your shoe.
c) A note saying, 'The Phantom Pooer Strikes Again'.
d) I shall complain to the RSPCA about this book.

26. Who holds the record for going to the toilet at the highest altitude?

a) An Everest expedition member.
b) An American astronaut.
c) A Russian astronaut.
d) ET.

27. Which of the following is used to make jelly?

a) Horse manure.
b) The insides of a whale.
c) Snail's eyeballs.
d) Yuk, I'm beginning to feel sick.

28. How do you get snot off clothes?

a) Scrape it off.
b) Eat it off.
c) It depends if it's all in one lump.
d) I definitely think I'm going to throw up.

29. What is the best way to eat maggots?

a) Inside an apple.
b) Raw with garlic.
c) With a fork.
d) I don't know, I'm a vegetarian.

30. Which is the most unhygienic part of a house?

a) The lavatory bowl.
b) The kitchen sink.
c) The bit behind the settee where everyone sticks their nose-pickings.
d) The doormat.

31. A dog thinks you are a tree and pees against your leg. Do you:

a) Kick the dog?
b) Pee on it in revenge?
c) Tell your friends it's a new perfume?
d) Pretend it didn't happen?

32. Where can you find the biggest load of wind?

a) The zoo.
b) The Houses of Parliament.
c) In your underwear.
d) A hot air balloon.

(For how to score *see* page 88.)

Yuk Quiz 1 Scoring

Question 1.
a) 3 points
b) 6 points
c) 10 points
d) 0 points

Question 2.
a) 3 points
b) 6 points
c) 10 points
d) 0 points

Question 3.
a) 3 points
b) 6 points
c) 10 points
d) 0 points

Question 4.
a) 3 points
b) 6 points
c) 10 points
d) 0 points

Question 5.
a) 3 points
b) 6 points
c) 10 points
d) 0 points

Question 6.
a) 0 points
b) 10 points
c) 6 points
d) 0 points

Question 7.
a) 3 points
b) 3 points
c) 10 points
d) 6 points

Question 8.
a) 3 points
b) 3 points
c) 10 points
d) 6 points

Question 9.
a) 6 points
b) 6 points
c) 10 points
d) 3 points

Question 10.
a) 0 points
b) 0 points
c) 0 points
d) 10 points

Question 11.
a) 0 points
b) 3 points
c) 6 points
d) 10 points

Question 12.
a) 6 points
b) 3 points
c) 10 points
d) 0 points

Question 13.
a) 6 points
b) 10 points
c) 3 points
d) 0 points

Question 14.
a) 3 points
b) 10 points
c) 10 points
d) 0 points

Question 15.
a) 6 points
b) 3 points
c) 10 points
d) 0 points

Question 16.
a) 3 points
b) 6 points
c) 10 points
d) 0 points

Question 17.
a) 6 points
b) 6 points
c) 10 points
d) 0 points

Question 18.
a) 3 points
b) 6 points
c) 10 points
d) 3 points

Question 19.
a) 10 points
b) 10 points
c) 10 points
d) 0 points

Question 20.
a) 3 points
b) 3 points
c) 10 points
d) 0 points

Question 21.
a) 0 points
b) 0 points
c) 0 points
d) 10 points

Question 22.
a) 3 points
b) 6 points
c) 10 points
d) 0 points

Question 23.
a) 3 points
b) 10 points
c) 10 points
d) 0 points

Question 24.
a) 3 points
b) 6 points
c) 10 points
d) 3 points

Question 25.
a) 3 points
b) 10 points
c) 6 points
d) 0 points

Question 26.
a) 3 points
b) 3 points
c) 3 points
d) 6 points

Question 27.
a) 3 points
b) 3 points
c) 3 points
d) 0 points

Question 28.
a) 3 points
b) 6 points
c) 10 points
d) 0 points

Question 29.
a) 6 points
b) 10 points
c) 10 points
d) 0 points

Question 30.
a) 3 points
b) 3 points
c) 10 points
d) 3 points

Question 31.
a) 6 points
b) 10 points
c) 3 points
d) 0 points

Question 32.
a) 3 points
b) 6 points
c) 10 points
d) 0 points.

Check Your Yuk Rating – How did you score?

Over 321 points – You are either a liar or bad at adding up.

320 points – You are the most disgusting person in the world.

250-319 points – Yuk! How do people stand you?

150-249 points – You have a strong stomach and a disgusting mind.

50-149 points – You're pretending to be nicer than you really are.

0-49 points – Wimp.

MY OWN PERSONAL DISGUSTING YUK APPENDIX

My own most disgusting habit is . . . .
. . . .
. . . .
. . . .

The most digusting person I know is . . . .
. . . .   because
. . . .
. . . .
. . . .

The most disgusting living thing I can think of is

. . . .
. . . .

The most disgusting dead thing I can think of is

. . . .
. . . .

The most disgusting object I can think of is

. . . .

. . . .

. . . .

The most disgusting food I can imagine is

. . . .

. . . .

. . . .

The most disgusting article of clothing ever would be

. . . .

. . . .

. . . .

The most disgusting habit I can imagine is . . . . . .

. . . .

. . . .

TAKE A DEEP BREATH AND REACH FOR THE SMELLING SALTS BEFORE ENTERING THE RED FOX JOKE ZONE - HOME OF THE SMELLIEST JOKES AROUND!

THE SMELLY SOCKS JOKE BOOK

Susan Abbott

Packed with pungent puns and reeking with revolting riddles, it's guaranteed to leave you gasping for air!

ISBN 0 09 956270 7   £2.99

THE EVEN SMELLIER SOCKS JOKE BOOK

Karen King

The pongiest and most putrid collection of gagtastic gags you'll ever come across. Guaranteed to make you laugh till you hurl!

ISBN 0 09 926513 3   £2.99

WARNING: THEY STINK!

FROM CHRISTMAS CRACK-UPS TO EGG-CELLANT EGG JOKES, THEY'RE ALL HERE I THE RED FOX JOKE BOOKS!

SANTA'S CHRISTMAS JOKE BOOK

Katie Wales

You'll be giggling over your turkey
and groaning under the mistletoe with
this crazy collection of Christmas corkers

ISBN 0 09 926703 9   £2.99

THE GOOD EGG YOLK BOOK

Katie Wales

Eggs-actly what you need
to become an
eggs-pert joker!

It'll crack you up!

ISBN 0 09 965960 3   £2.99